PURCELL

Ode on St Cecilia's Day 1692

HAIL ! BRIGHT CECILIA

for soprano, two altos, tenor &
two basses soli, SSAATB & instruments

Edited by Peter Dennison

vocal score

Order No: NOV 072309

NOVELLO PUBLISHING LIMITED

CONTENTS

INTRODUCTION

This new edition of the vocal score is issued uniform with that of the full score published as volume 8 of the Purcell Society edition. Suggested editorial modifications of rhythm in the solo vocal parts are shown by superscript stems, or by a smaller stem on the shorter of the two notes involved. These modifications in the chorus and keyboard parts have been incorporated straight into the text for the sake of practical clarity, but a clear distinction between the original and these modifications is given in the full score. Any trills or notes printed small are editorial. Some alternative readings are provided in full-sized type. These are by Purcell himself, and their sources are specified. No distinction is made in the vocal score between original and editorial tempo and dynamic markings, or accidentals details of which are found in the full score.

The keyboard part is of two kinds. In the large concerted movements it is a reduction of the parts although missing notes that are vital to the harmony and which the continuo would have played, such as thirds of chords, have been included in small type. It is suggested that in performances with the full ensemble the keyboard player should devise a simple continuo part from this, and should play only where the continuo line is marked 'accompanied'; in passages marked 'unaccompanied' the keyboard should remain silent. In other movements the keyboard has a true continuo part. This has been designed for organ, and when it is played on the harpsichord many of the ties should be omitted and the texture should be thickened. The lowest part of the keyboard is given at the pitch of the original continuo line, and all the figuring of the latter from the full score has been included. A complete keyboard continuo part is included in the full score.

Cambridge
1975

PETER DENNISON

ODE ON ST CECILIA'S DAY 1692

25
30
Unaccompanied
Tpt
Tpt
Accompanied
p Str
35
Str
Tpt
Tpt
40
f
Unaccompanied
Accompanied
45

Adagio
Vln
p
50
Ob
Unaccompanied
Vla
55
Vln
Accompanied
60
Ob
Unaccompanied
Vla
65
Vln
Accompanied
Ob
Unaccompanied
Vln
70
Accompanied
75
Ob
Unaccompanied
80
Str
cresc
Accompanied
85
Tutti
90
Repeat the Canzona and the Adagio
tr
dim

Allegro
95
Tpt & Ob
f Unaccompanied
Vln & Ob
Vla
100
Accompanied
105
110
115
120
125

130
f
135
140
Tpt & Dr
mp Str
Unaccompanied
Accom-
panied
Unaccompanied
145
f Accompanied
Fine
Grave
Str & Ob
150
f
155
p cresc
dim
D.𝄋 al fine

2 SOLOS AND CHORUS HAIL! BRIGHT CECILIA

Hail! Hail! Hail! Hail!
mp 2 COUNTERTENORS
Hail! Hail! Hail! Hail! Fill ev - 'ry heart with love of
Hail! Hail! Hail! Hail!
Hail! Hail! Hail! Hail!
mp Unaccompanied
15
4 TREBLES mp
Fill ev - 'ry
thee and thy ce - les - - - tial Art, thy
mp 2 TENORS
Fill ev - 'ry heart with love of thee and thy ce - les - -
heart with love of thee and thy ce - les - tial Art, thy ce -
ce - les - tial Art, fill ev - 'ry
- - tial Art, with love of thee, with love of thee and thy ce -
2 BASSES mp
Fill ev - 'ry heart with love of thee and thy ce -
Accompanied
6 6 #6

les - tial Art, fill ev - 'ry heart with love of thee and thy ce -
heart with love of thee and thy ce - les - tial Art, and thy ce -
les - tial Art, and thy ce - les - tial Art,
les - tial Art, fill ev - 'ry
20
les - - - - - - - - - -
les - - tial, thy ce - les - tial Art, fill ev - 'ry
fill ev - 'ry heart with love of thee and thy ce -
heart with love of thee and thy ce - les - tial Art,

mf CHORUS
tial Art, Fill ev - 'ry heart with
mf CHORUS
heart with love of thee, Fill ev - 'ry heart with love of thee,
mf CHORUS
les - - - tial Art, Fill ev - 'ry heart with love of
mf CHORUS
and thy ce - les - tial Art, Fill ev - 'ry
mf
25
love of thee and thy ce - les - tial Art.
fill ev - 'ry heart with love of thee and thy ce - les - tial Art.
thee and thy ce - les - tial, thy ce - les - tial Art.
heart with love of thee, with love of thee and thy ce - les - tial Art.
mp
Unaccomp-
anied
Accompanied
mp

30
35
Fill ev-'ry
Fill ev-'ry heart with love of thee and thy
Fill ev - 'ry heart with love of
Fill ev - 'ry heart with love of thee and thy ce -
heart with love of thee and thy ce - les - tial Art,
ce - les - tial Art, fill ev - 'ry
thee and thy ce - les - tial Art,

les - - - tial Art, fill ev - 'ry
fill ev - 'ry heart with love of thee,
heart with love of thee, with love of thee, fill ev - 'ry heart with
fill ev - 'ry heart with
6 4 5 #3 6 4 7 #3
40
heart with love of thee and thy ce - les - - tial Art.
SOLO
p
fill ev-'ry heart with love of thee and thy ce-les - tial Art. That
love of thee and thy ce-les - tial Art.
love of thee and thy ce - les - tial Art.
Continuo
p

45
thine and Mu - - - - - - sic's sa - cred
p SOLO
That thine and Mu - - - - sic's sa - cred
mf CHORUS
love, May make the Brit - ish for - est prove as fa - mous, as fa - mous,
mf CHORUS
love, May make the Brit - ish for - est prove, as fa - mous, as
mf CHORUS
May make the Brit - ish for - est prove, as fa - mous, as
Reduction
mf

50
p SOLO
That thine and Mu -
as fa-mous as Do-do-na's vo - cal_ grove.
fa-mous, fa-mous as Do-do-na's vo - cal grove.
fa-mous, fa-mous as Do-do-na's vo - cal grove.
p SOLO
That thine and
Continuo
p
tr
f CHORUS
- - - - - sic's sa - cred love, May make the
f CHORUS
May make the
f CHORUS
May make the
tr
f CHORUS
Mu - - - - sic's sa - cred love, May make the
Reduction
f

55
Brit - ish for - est prove as fa - mous, as fa - mous, as fa - mous
Brit - ish for - est prove, as fa - mous, as fa - mous, fa - mous
Brit - ish for - est prove, as fa - mous, as fa - mous, fa - mous
Brit - ish for - est prove, as fa - mous, as fa - mous, fa - mous
as Do - do - na's vo - cal grove, as fa - mous, as
as Do - do - na's vo - cal grove, as fa - mous, as fa - mous,
as Do - do - na's vo - cal grove, as fa - mous, as
as Do - do - na's vo - cal grove, as fa - mous, as

60
famous, as famous as Dodona's vocal grove.
as famous, as famous as Dodona's vocal grove.
famous, as famous as Dodona's vocal grove.
famous, as famous as Dodona's vocal grove.
Str & Ob
Unaccompanied
Accompanied
65
70
tr
attacca

3 DUET HARK EACH TREE

Andante

Continuo

mf

Reduction

Vln

Fl

Vln Fl Vln Fl Vln Fl

BASS

mf

Hark, hark each Tree, its si - - - lence

Vln

Bar 13: If there is a Bass Flute present, the passages enclosed in half brackets in the lower stave of the keyboard part should be played an octave higher.

ALTO
mf
35
Hark, hark each Tree, its si - - - lence
breaks, hark,
Fl
7
40
breaks, hark, hark each Tree, its si - - - lence
hark each Tree, its si - - - - lence
Vln
Fl
Vln
Fl
45
breaks,
breaks, hark,
p
Vln
Fl
Vln
Fl
Vln
Fl
Vln
p

30
55
p
hark,
hark each Tree, its si - - - lence breaks,
Fl
7
#
hark each Tree, its si - - lence breaks, hark,
60
hark, hark each
Vln
7
#
hark each Tree, its si - - - lence
65
Tree, its si - - - - - lence
Fl
Vln
Fl

mf
70
breaks, The Box and Fir, to talk,
mf
breaks, The Box and Fir, to talk,
Continuo
mf
75
to talk, to talk, to talk be-
to talk, to talk, to talk be -
f
80
gin.
Hark, hark,
f
gin. Hark, hark, hark,
Reduction
f
Fl
Vln
Fl
Vln

hark,
hark,
hark,
hark,
hark,
hark,
This in the
Fl
Vln
85
spright - - - - ly
90
That in the Flute dis-tinct-ly, dis - tinct - ly
Vi - o-lin,
Fl

95
speaks, dis - tinct-ly, dis - tinct - ly speaks,
mf
This in the
Vln
#6
5
100
spright - - - - ly
mf
that in the Flute dis -
tr
mf
Vi - o-lin, this in the spright - -
Fl
mf
105
Tutti

110
tinct-ly, dis - tinct-ly, dis - tinct - ly speaks.
- - ly Vi-o-lin, dis - tinct - ly speaks.
Vln
Fl
Vln
Fl
Vln
Fl
Vln
115
mf
'Twas Sym-pa-thy their
mf
'Twas Sym-pa-thy, 'twas Sym-pa-thy, twas
Fl
Vln
Continuo

120
list-'ning Breth - ren drew, 'twas Sym - -
Sym-pa - thy, 'twas Sym - - - pa-thy their
125
- pa-thy their list - 'ning Breth-ren drew, When to the Thra-cian
list - - 'ning Breth-ren drew,
130
lyre, with lea-fy wings they flew,
When to the Thra-cian lyre, when

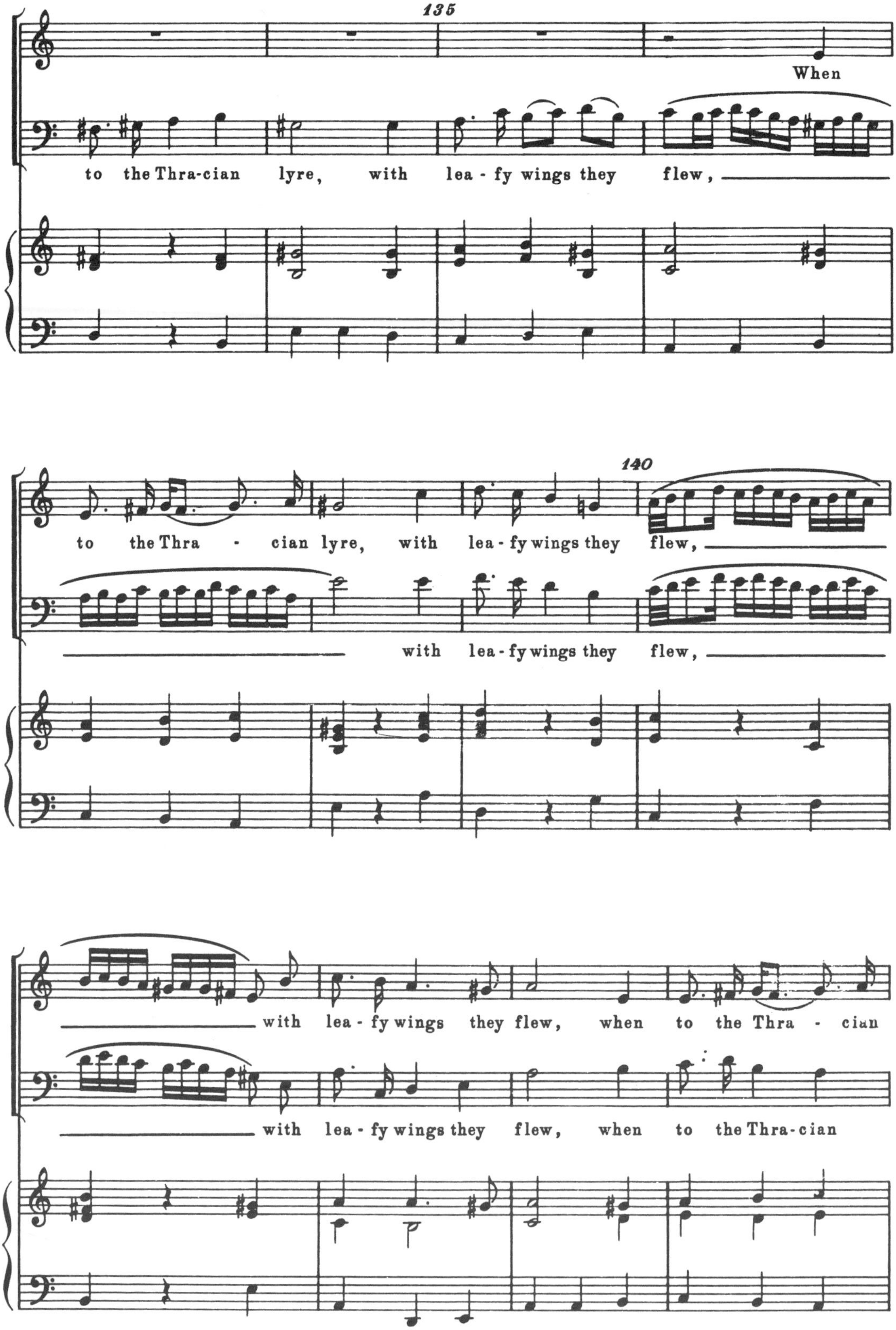
135
When
to the Thra-cian lyre, with lea - fy wings they flew,
140
to the Thra - cian lyre, with lea - fy wings they flew,
with lea - fy wings they flew,
with lea - fy wings they flew, when to the Thra - cian
with lea - fy wings they flew, when to the Thra-cian

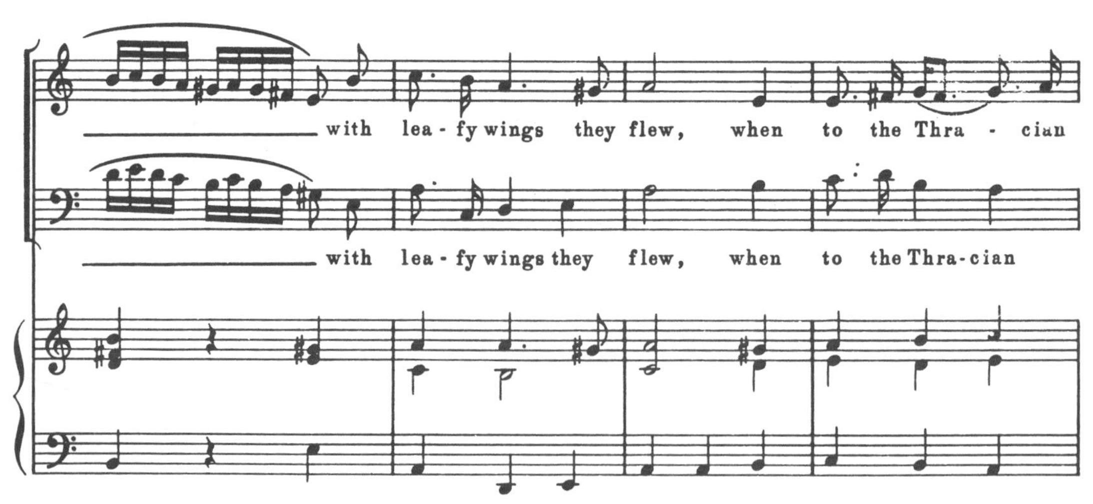

145
lyre, with lea - fy wings they flew, with
lyre, with lea - fy wings they flew, with
150
p
lea - fy wings they flew, with lea - fy wings they flew.
p
lea - fy wings they flew, with lea - fy wings they flew.
Reduction
Vln
p
f
Fl
Vln
Fl
155
Fl
Vln
Vln
Fl
160
attacca

4 SOLO 'TIS NATURE'S VOICE

Bars 5-6: Alternative from Purcell's later autograph.

The u - ni - ver - sal tongue, the u - ni - ver - sal tongue, to none of all her
4
2
6
#7
tr
15
nu - m'rous race un - known. From her, from her it learnt, the
b3
#
might - y, the might - y, the might - y
tr
7
#6
20
art, To court the ear, or strike, or strike
#
b
#4
2
6
7

Bar 26: Alternative from Purcell's later autograph.

Bar 42: Alternative from Purcell's later autograph.

Bar 47: Purcell's direction

attacca

5 CHORUS SOUL OF THE WORLD

Bar 6. T.: Purcell's alternative: spired, in-spired by

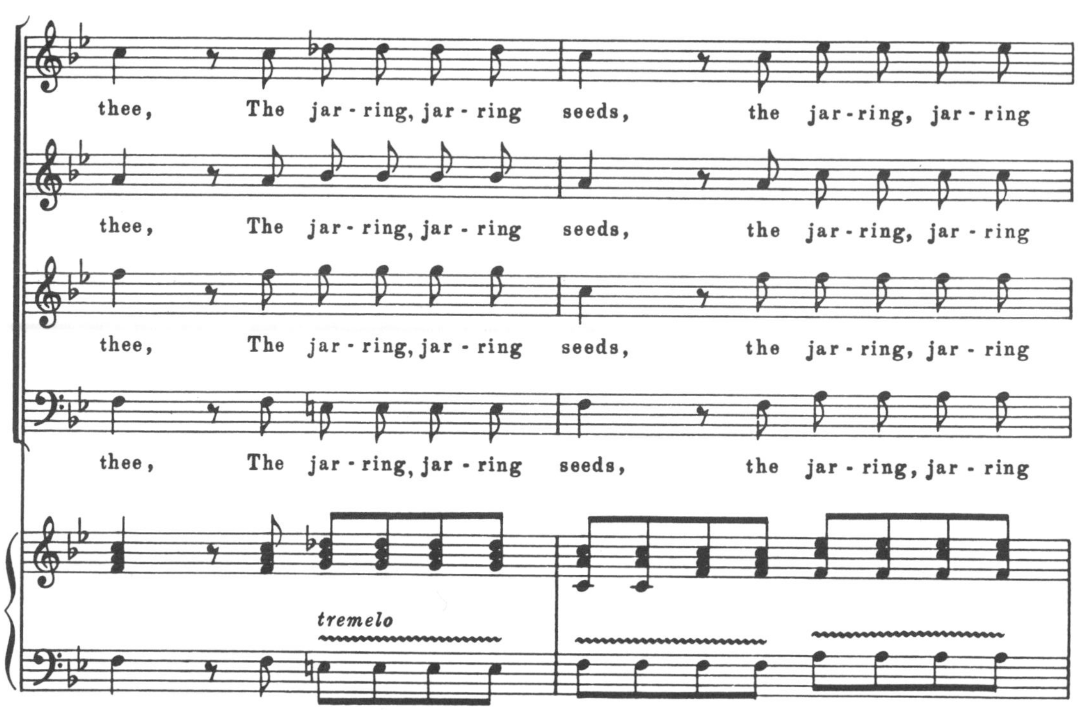

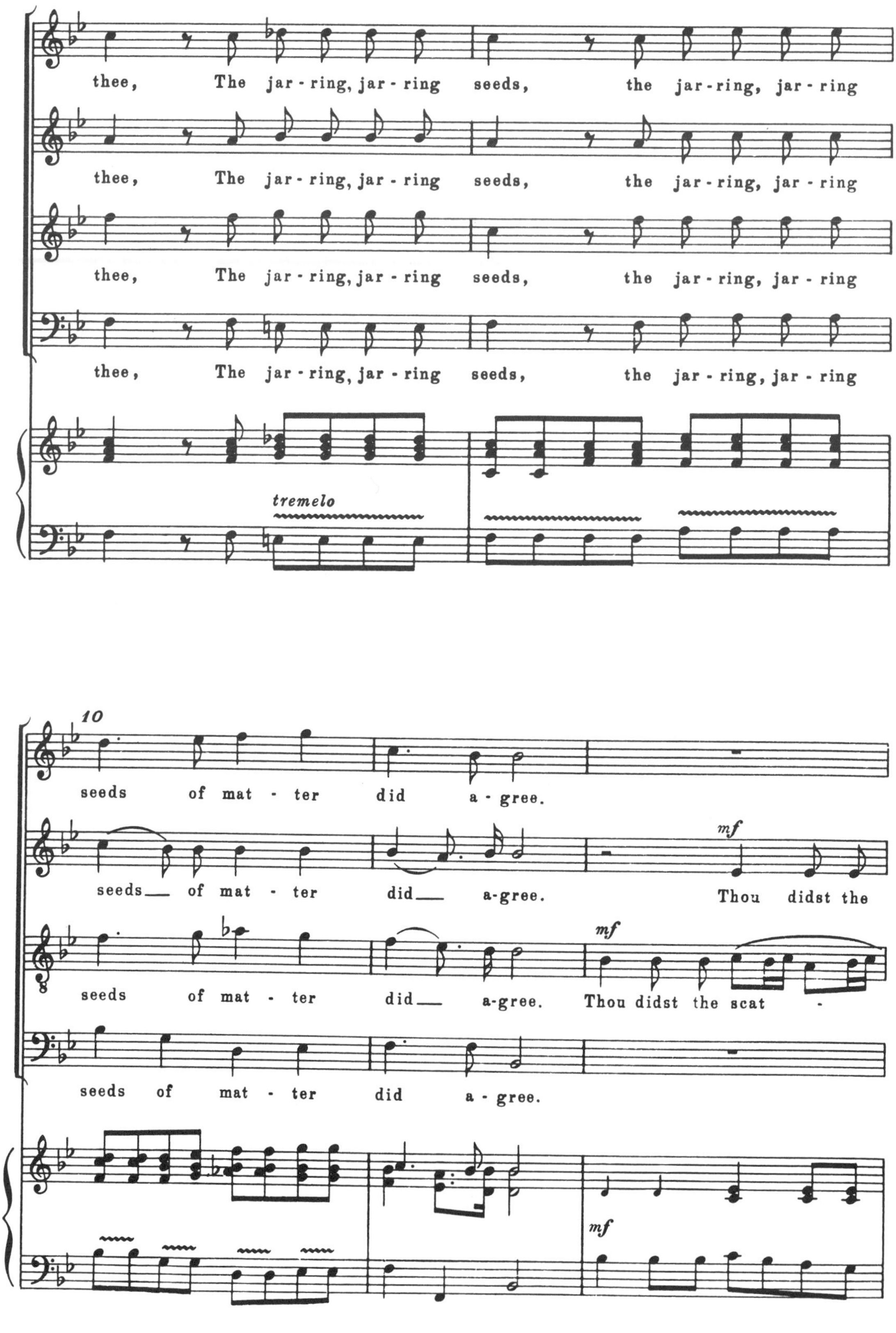
thee, The jar - ring, jar - ring seeds, the jar - ring, jar - ring
thee, The jar - ring, jar - ring seeds, the jar - ring, jar - ring
thee, The jar - ring, jar - ring seeds, the jar - ring, jar - ring
thee, The jar - ring, jar - ring seeds, the jar - ring, jar - ring
tremelo
10
seeds of mat - ter did a - gree.
mf
seeds__ of mat - ter did__ a-gree. Thou didst the
mf
seeds of mat - ter did__ a-gree. Thou didst the scat -
seeds of mat - ter did a - gree.
mf

mf
Thou didst the scat - -
scat - - - ter'd a - toms
- - - - -
♮6 ♮
15
- - - ter'd a - toms bind,
bind, the scat - ter'd, scat - ter'd a - toms bind,
- ter'd a - toms bind, thou didst the scat -
mf
Thou didst the scat - - -

thou didst the scat - - -

thou didst the scat - -

- - - ter'd a - toms bind,

- - - ter'd a toms bind,

20

- - - - -

- - - ter'd a - toms bind,

thou didst the scat -

thou didst the scat - - -

- ter'd, the scat - ter'd a - toms bind,
thou didst the scat - ter'd a - toms bind,
- - ter'd, scat - ter'd a - toms bind,
- - ter'd, scat - ter'd a - toms bind,
mf
mf
which by thy laws, of true pro - por - tion joined,
mf
which by thy laws, of true pro - por-tion joined,
mf
which by thy laws, of true pro - por - tion joined,
mf
which by thy laws, of true pro - por - tion joined,

25
mf
which by thy laws, of true pro-por - tion joined. Made up of va -
mf
which by thy laws, of true pro-por - tion joined. Made up of
which by thy laws, of true pro-por - tion joined.
which by thy laws, of true pro-por-tion joined.
mf
Unaccompanied
30
- - - rious parts, made up of
va - - rious parts, made up of va -
mf
Made up of va - - rious parts,
mf
Made up of va - rious parts,
Accompanied

va - rious parts, of va - rious, va -
- rious parts,
made up of va -
made up of va - rious parts,
made up of
made up of va - rious parts,
made up of va -
35
- rious parts,
made up of va -
- rious parts,
made up of va -
va - rious parts, made up of va - -
- - rious parts,
cresc

f

- - rious parts, one per-fect, one per-fect, one

f

- rious, va-rious parts, of va-rious parts, one per-fect, one per-fect,

f

- - rious parts, one per-fect, one per-fect,

f cresc

made up of va - rious parts, one per-fect, one, one per - fect,

f

40

cresc

per - - fect, per - fect har - mo-ny.

cresc

one per - fect, per - fect har - mo-ny.

cresc

one per - - fect, per-fect har - mo-ny.

per - - - fect har - mo-ny.

6 SOLO AND CHORUS THOU TUN'ST THIS WORLD

35
SOPRANO
mf(p)
Thou tun'st this world, this world be - low, the
Continuo
mf(p)
spheres a - bove, the spheres a - bove,
40
mf(p)
Who in the heaven - ly round to their
45
mf(p)
own mu - sic move,
50

55
to their own mu - sic move, who in the
heaven - ly round to their
60
own mu - sic move,
65
to their own mu - sic move.

CHORUS
SOPRANO
mf (p)
70
Thou tun'st this world, this world be - low, the
ALTO
mf (p)
Thou tun'st this world, this world be - low, the
TENOR
mf (p)
Thou tun'st this world be - low, the spheres a-
BASS
mf (p)
Thou tun'st this world be - low, the spheres a-
Reduction
Str & Ob
mf (p)
75
spheres a - bove, the spheres a - bove,
spheres a - bove, the spheres a - bove,
bove, the spheres a - bove, the spheres a - bove,
bove, the spheres a - bove, the spheres a - bove,

mf (p)

80

Who in the heaven - ly round to their

Who in the heaven - ly round to their

Who in the heaven - ly round to their

Who in the heaven - ly round to their

own mu - sic move,

85

own mu - sic move,

own mu - sic move,

own mu - sic move,

— to their own mu - sic move, who in the heaven - ly —

— to their own mu - sic move, who in the heaven - ly,

— to their own mu - sic move, who in the heaven - ly —

— to their own mu - sic move, who in the heaven - ly —

round ——— to their own mu - sic

heaven - ly round ——— to their own mu - sic

round ——— to their own mu - sic

round ——— to their own mu - sic

95
cresc
move,
cresc
move,
cresc
move,
cresc
move,
cresc
100
f
to their own_ mu - sic_ move. move.
f
to their own_ mu-sic move. move.
f
to their own mu - sic move. move.
f
to their own mu-sic move. move.
1
2
f

7 TRIO WITH THAT SUBLIME CELESTIAL LAY

10
If a-ny earth-ly mu-sic dare, if a-ny earth-ly mu-sic
If a-ny earth-ly mu-sic
- ble Or - gan may,
tr
6
dare, The no-ble Or-gan, the no-ble, no - -
dare, The no-ble Or-gan, the no-ble, no - -
The no-ble Or-gan, the no-ble, no - - -
15
- - ble Or - gan may.
- - ble Or - gan may.
- - ble Or - gan may. From heav'n its won - drous, won - drous
tr

20
From heav'n its won - drous, won - drous notes were given,
From heav'n its won - drous, won - drous notes were given,
mf
notes were given, Ce - ci - lia
mf
mf
Ce - ci - lia oft con-vers'd with heav'n, Ce - ci - lia
mf
Ce - ci - lia oft con-vers'd with heav'n, Ce - ci - lia oft con-vers'd with
oft con-vers'd with heav'n, Ce - ci - lia oft con-vers'd with heav'n, Ce - ci - lia
25
oft con-vers'd with heav'n, Ce - ci - lia oft con - vers'd with heav'n.
mp
heav'n, Ce - ci - lia oft con-vers'd, Ce - ci - lia oft con-vers'd with heav'n, Some An-gel
oft con-vers'd, Ce - ci - lia oft, oft con - vers'd with heav'n.
mp

30
of — the sa - cred quire, Did with his breath the pipes in-spire, and, of their notes a -
bove, the just re-sem-blance, the just re-sem-blance, the just — re - sem-blance gave.
tr
Brisk
35 mf
Brisk, brisk, — brisk with-out light-ness, with-out dul-ness grave,
40
mf
Brisk, brisk, — brisk with-out light-ness, with - out dul-ness grave,
mf
Brisk, — brisk, brisk with-out light-ness, with-out dul-ness grave,
Brisk
mf

45
f
grave, grave, with-out dul-ness grave, brisk,__ brisk_with-out
grave, grave, with-out dul-ness grave, brisk,__ brisk_with-out
grave, grave, with-out dul-ness grave, brisk, brisk_with-out
50
light-ness, brisk, brisk_ with-out light-ness, with-out dul-ness
light-ness, brisk, brisk_ with-out_ light-ness, with-out dul-ness
light-ness, brisk, brisk_ with-out light-ness, with-out dul-ness
55
p
grave, grave, grave, with-out dul-ness grave, with-out dul-ness grave.
grave, grave, grave, with-out dul-ness grave, with-out dul-ness grave.
grave, grave, grave, with-out dul-ness grave, with-out dul-ness grave.

8
SOLO WONDROUS MACHINE
Moderato
Ob
Reduction
mf
BASS
p
cresc
f
Won - drous, won - drous, won - drous, won - drous machine, won - drous, won - drous,
won - drous, won - drous ma - chine, to thee the

war - - - - - bling
lute though used to con - quest, must be forced, must be forced, must be forced to
20
yield, must be forced, must be forced, must be forced to_ yield, must be forced, must be forced to
yield, must be forced, must be forced, must be forced to_ yield.

25
mf
With thee un - a - ble, with thee un - a - ble,
mf
with thee un - a - - - - -
30
- - - - ble to dis - pute.
Though used to con - quest,
tr

35
though used to con-quest, is with thee_ un-a - ble_ to dis-pute.
mf
p
Won - drous,
40
cresc
won - drous, won - drous, won - drous ma -
cresc
f
f
mf
chine, to thee the war - - -
mf

45
bling lute, though used to con - quest,
must be forced, must be forced, must be forced to yield, must be forced, must be forced, must be forced to
yield, must be forced, must be forced to yield, must be forced, must be forced, must be forced to
50
yield.

9 SOLO THE AIRY VIOLIN

strings, To court the cru - el fair, to court the cru - el_ fair, or
praise vic - to - - - rious kings.
Whilst all — thy con-se-cra - ted
lays, whilst all — thy con-se-cra - ted lays Are to more no - ble, no -

45
- ble u - ses_ bent. And ev - 'ry grate-ful note to heav'n re-pays The
50
p
me-lo-dy, the me-lo-dy, the me-lo-dy it_ lent, And ev - 'ry grate-ful
p
55
note to heav'n_ re - pays The me - lo-dy, the me - lo-dy, the
60
me-lo-dy it_ lent.
attacca

10 DUET IN VAIN THE AM'ROUS FLUTE

TENOR
mp
20
In vain the am - - - 'rous
Continuo
2
ALTO
mp
25
In vain the am - - - 'rous
flute, in vain the am - 'rous flute and soft,
30
flute, and soft gui - tar, Joint-ly, joint - ly la -
soft gui - tar, Joint-ly, joint - ly
4
35
- - - - - bour,
la - - - - bour, to in-
mf
mf

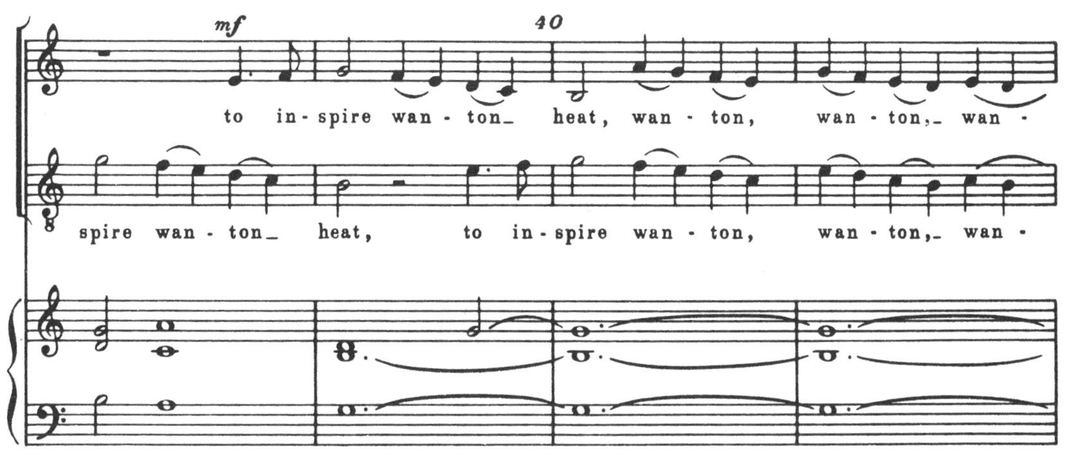
mf
40
to in-spire wan-ton_ heat, wan-ton, wan-ton,_ wan-
spire wan-ton_ heat, to in-spire wan-ton, wan-ton,_ wan-

45
1
2
-ton_ heat and loose_ de-sire, sire.
-ton_ heat_ and loose_ de-sire, In sire.
p

p
50
Whilst thy chaste airs do gent-ly, gent-ly, gent-ly_ move,
p
Whilst thy chaste

55
mf
do gent - ly, gent - ly, gent - ly move, Se-ra-phic
airs do gent - ly, gent - ly, gent - ly move,
mf
60
flames and heav'n - ly love, and heav'n - ly love, Se-ra-phic
mf
Se-ra-phic flames and heav'n - ly love, Se-ra-phic flames and
65
tr
flames and heav'n - - - - ly
tr
heav'n - ly love, heav'n - - - ly

mp
70
love. Whilst thy chaste airs do gent - ly, gent - ly,
love.
mp
75
gent - ly_ move, do gent - ly, gent - ly,
mp
Whilst thy chaste airs do gent - ly, gent - ly,
f
80
gent - ly_ move, Se-ra-phic flames and heav'n - ly love, and
f
gent - ly_ move, Se-ra-phic flames and heav'n - ly
f

85
heav'n - ly love, Se-ra-phic flames and heav'n -
love, Se-ra-phic flames and heav'n - ly love, heav'n -
tr
90
- - - - ly love.
- - - - ly love.
Reduction
Fl
f
95
100
tr

11 SOLO THE FIFE AND ALL THE HARMONY OF WAR

and all, all, all, all, all, all the har - - - - mo - ny of
2
20
war,
and all, all, all,
f
mp
2
all, all the har - - - - mo - ny of war, In vain,
25
in vain at-tempt the pas - sions, the pas - sions, the

30
pas - - - sions to a - larm,
f
— a-larm, a-larm, a - larm, a - larm,
In vain at-tempt the
35
pas - sions, the pas - sions, the pas - - sions to a -
larm,
a-larm, a-larm, a - larm, a - larm,
f

40
mf
Which thy com - mand - ing sounds,
mf
com-pose and charm,
45
which thy com-mand-ing sounds,
2
which thy com-mand-ing sounds,
50
sounds, sounds,
6

Bars 55-57: Alternative from Purcell's later autograph

Bars 67-69: Alternative from Purcell's later autograph

5
let these a-mongst them-selves con-test, Which can dis-charge its
mongst them-selves con-test, Which can dis-charge its sin-gle du -
4 3
sin-gle du - ty best, which can dis-charge its sin-gle du - -
- - - - ty best, which can dis-charge its sin-gle du -
10
- - - - - - ty best:
- - - - - - ty best:
1
1

best: Thou summ'st their diff-'ring, diff-'ring gra-ces up in
best: Thou summ'st their diff-'ring, diff-'ring gra-ces up in one, thou summ'st their
one, thou summ'st their diff - 'ring, diff - 'ring gra - -
diff-'ring, diff - 'ring gra-ces, summ'st their diff - 'ring, diff - 'ring gra - -
- - - - - - ces up in one, And art a
- - - - - - ces up in one,

mp
con-sort, and art a con-sort of _ them all, all, all, all, all, all
And art a con-sort, art a con-sort of _ them all, all, all, all, all, all
25
mf
with-in thy-self a-lone, and art a con-sort, art a
with-in thy-self a-lone, and art a con-sort, and art a
cresc
con-sort of _ them all, all, all, all, all, all, all, all, all, all, all
con-sort of _ them all, all, all, all, all, all, all, all, all with-
30
with-in thy-self a-lone. lone.
in thy-self a-lone. Thou summ'st their lone.

13 CHORUS AND QUARTET HAIL! BRIGHT CECILIA

Hail!
Hail!
Hail!
Hail!
Hail!
Hail!
Hail!
Hail!
Ob
Vln
10
Hail!
Hail! Hail bright Ce-
Hail!
Hail! Hail bright Ce-
Hail!
Hail! Hail bright Ce-
Hail!
Hail! Hail bright Ce-
Ob
Tpt
ci - lia, hail to thee!
15
ci - lia, hail to thee! Great,
ci - lia, hail to thee! Great,
ci - lia, hail to thee! Great,
Str
Ob

Great, great, great Pa - tro - ness, great
great, great Pa - tro -
great, great Pa - tro -
great, great Pa - tro - ness,
Tpt Str & Ob
20
Pa - tro - ness of us, of us, of us, of
ness, great Pa - tro - ness of us, of us, of us, of
ness, great Pa - tro - ness of us, of us, of us, of
great Pa - tro - ness of us, of us, of us, of
25
us, great Pa - tro - ness, great Pa - tro - ness of us and Har - mo - ny.
us, great Pa - tro - ness of us and Har - mo - ny.
us, great Pa - tro - ness of us and Har - mo - ny.
us, great Pa - tro - ness of us and Har - mo - ny.
Drum

[A little slower]
SOPRANO 1
SOPRANO 2
ALTO 1
mf
Thou dost thy for - mer
ALTO 2
mf
Who whilst a -
TENOR
mf
Who whilst a - mong the choir a - bove,
BASS mf
Who whilst a - mong the choir a - bove, who whilst a - mong the choir a -
[A little slower]
Ob
mf
28
mf
Who whilst a - mong the choir a - bove, the choir a - bove,
mf
Who whilst a - mong the choir a - bove,
skill im - prove, Who whilst a -
mong the choir a - bove,
Thou dost thy for - mer skill, thou dost thy for - mer,
bove, Thou dost thy for - mer skill im -

30
Thou dost thy for - mer skill im - prove,
who whilst a - mong the choir a - bove,
mong the choir a - bove,
who whilst a -
who whilst a - mong the choir a - bove, Thou dost thy for - mer
for - mer skill im - prove,
prove,
Who whilst a - mong the choir a -
thou dost thy
Thou dost thy for - mer skill im - prove,
mong the choir a - bove,
Thou dost thy for - mer,
skill im - prove,
thou dost thy for - mer
Who whilst a - mong the choir a - bove, Thou dost thy
bove, who whilst a - mong the choir a - bove, Thou dost thy for - mer,

35
for - mer skill im - prove.
thou dost thy for - mer skill im-prove.
for - mer skill im-prove.
skill im - prove.
for - mer skill im - prove.
for - mer skill im - prove.
Tpt
f Ob&Str Unaccompanied
Accom-panied
mf
Who whilst a-mong the choir a - bove,
mf
Thou dost thy for - mer
mf
Who whilst a-mong the choir a -
f
Who whilst a -
f

40
mf
Who whilst a-mong the choir a - bove, Thou dost thy
mf
Thou dost thy for - mer skill im - prove,
Who whilst a-mong the choir a -
skill im - prove,
bove, Thou dost thy for - mer skill im -
mong the choir a -
cresc
for - mer skill, thou dost thy for - mer skill, thou dost thy
f
cresc
thou dost thy for - mer skill im -
cresc
bove, Thou dost thy for - mer skill, thou dost thy for - mer
f
cresc
thou dost thy for - mer skill, thou dost thy for -
f
cresc
prove, Who whilst a-mong the choir a - bove, a - bove,
bove, a - bove,
cresc

45
for - mer skill im - prove, thy for-mer skill im-prove.
prove, thou dost thy for-mer skill im - prove, thy for-mer skill im-prove.
skill im - prove, thou dost thy for-mer skill im-prove.
- - - - mer, for-mer skill im-prove.
Thou dost thy for - mer skill im - prove.
Thou dost thy for - mer, for - mer skill im-prove.
attacca
Slow
ALTO 1 SOLO
With rap-tures, rap - tures of de-
ALTO 2 SOLO
With rap-tures, rap - tures of de-
TENOR SOLO
With rap-tures, rap - tures of de-
BASS SOLO
With rap-tures, rap - tures of de-
Slow
Continuo

light dost see, Thy
light dost see, Thy fav-'rite Art make up,
light dost see, Thy fav-'rite Art make up, make up a part, thy
light dost see, Thy fav-'rite Art make up, make up a part,
fav-'rite Art make up, make up a part, Of in-fi-nite, in-fi-nite,
make up a part, Of in-fi-nite, in-fi-nite,
fav-'rite Art make up, make up a part, Of
thy fav-'rite Art make up a part Of
cresc
in - - - - fi-nite Fe-li-ci-ty.
cresc
in - - - - fi-nite Fe-li-ci-ty.
cresc
in-fi-nite, in-fi-nite, in - fi-nite Fe-li-ci-ty.
cresc
in-fi-nite, in-fi-nite, in-fi-nite, in - fi-nite Fe-li-ci-ty.
cresc
f

CHORUS
Tempo I
SOPRANO
ALTO
TENOR
BASS
f
Hail!
Tempo I
Vln
Ob
Reduction
f
65
Hail!
Tpt

Hail!
Hail!
Hail!
Hail!
Hail!
Hail!
Hail!
Hail!
Ob
Vln
70
Hail!
Hail!
Hail bright Ce -
Hail!
Hail!
Hail bright Ce -
Hail!
Hail!
Hail bright Ce -
Hail!
Hail!
Hail bright Ce -
Ob
Tpt

75
ci - lia, hail to thee!
ci - lia, hail to thee! Great,
ci - lia, hail to thee! Great,
ci - lia, hail to thee! Great,
Str
Ob
Great, great, great Pa - tro - ness, great
great, great Pa - tro -
great, great Pa - tro -
great, great Pa - tro - ness,
Tpt Str & Ob

Printed and bound in Great Britain by
Caligraving Limited Thetford Norfolk

3 4 5 6 7 8 9